THIS IS ~~MY~~ *His* STORY

THE POWER OF GOD
REVEALED IN YOUR LIFE

Mindy Kiker and Jenny Kochert

Welcome,

We're delighted you're here. Your presence with us signals a season of refreshing, a time to dig into the Bible and hear God speak.

You hold in your hands a **Flourish Bible Study Journal** which guides you to spend time in the Word, filling your mind and heart with His truth. When you discover He is good and you are called, you can walk fearlessly into the future.

We pray you will become *"like an olive tree flourishing in the house of God . . . trusting in God's unfailing love for ever and ever."* Psalm 52:8

Whatever the circumstances of your life right now, God's Word is waiting to meet you exactly where you are with the help you need to take the next step.

We all have seasons where we drift away from Jesus and His Word. It is easy to be distracted by the daily cares of life or to become embroiled in a fiery trial. This Bible Study Journal invites you to create a quiet space to cultivate confidence in your life right now. As you posture yourself to hear, you will receive the Word you need to step forward into the fulfillment of the promises God has spoken.

You are going to be amazed at what you discover as you pursue the daily practices of the DECLARE Bible Study Approach. One friend likens it to *"Holy Spirit sunglasses"* that allow you to see through the surface into the deep waters:

*I've been able to see deeper into the Bible than I've
ever done before. The Holy Spirit has used DECLARE
to bring much more life into my Bible time.*

As you practice the DECLARE Bible Study Approach, it will
become your own personal method to open any part of the
Bible with an expectation of hearing Jesus speak.

We created this **Flourish Bible Study Journal** from our
God-breathed desire to walk with you, to take the truth you
explore in Scripture and see it activated in your life. Regular
time with Jesus nourishes the seeds of hope with the soil
of truth, the sunshine of companionship, and the water of
prayer to ignite growth in your heart.

May the seeds planted in your life grow and flourish as you
open the Bible and enjoy time in God's presence. We stand
with you in expectation at how Jesus is going to show up in
your life as you feast on His Word.

HOW TO GET THE MOST OUT OF A FLOURISH BIBLE STUDY JOURNAL

Like most things in life, you get out what you put into it. Go
the gym, watch others do the heavy lifting, and not much is
going to happen to your muscles–but grab a set of dumbbells,
start reaching for the sky, and you'll see results!

We recommend you begin by committing to **Fight for Your
Fifteen**: set aside at least 15 minutes each day in Bible Study
and prayer. *"Commit to the Lord whatever you do, and he will
establish your plans."* (Proverbs 16:3)

This Bible Study Journal is designed to be completed in 20-days which takes a month at five days per week. But feel free to take longer or shorter depending on the time you have available. Each week is organized around a Declaration Verse which guides the five stages of the DECLARE Bible Study Approach: read & write, investigate, imagine, listen, and declare.

Within each day, three levels of study are offered depending on the time you have available:

 Today's DECLARE Practice
(can be completed in 10-15 minutes)

 Have a Little More Time?
(another 10-15 minutes)

 Digging Deeper
(another 10-15 minutes)

If you're strapped for time that day, just do **Today's DECLARE Practice** and skip **Have a Little More Time?** and **Digging Deeper**. No guilt. No pressure. Take each day as it comes, with your goal to *Fight for Your Fifteen*. Sometimes fifteen minutes is all you have and you won't make it past the first level.

If you have a medium amount of time, do the first two levels that day. If you have plenty of time, and the topic is intriguing, do all three levels. But take each day as it comes.

Now, we know that some of you are going to hate leaving blank spaces in your journal, and if you fall too far behind, you'll give up and stop altogether. We created these three levels with our less-is-more approach focusing on one Declaration Verse each week is to help you keep going. You're trying to develop your Bible Study muscles. Strength is built through daily consistency, not a huge burst of weightlifting and then nothing for days.

Please resist the Accuser who says you're doing a terrible job if you just do **Today's DECLARE Practice** and skip the other two levels. The study is designed with this flexibility to meet you in any season of life. A little bit is better than none.

The **Digging Deeper** part provides an optional reading plan. Notice the word "optional." Don't make it mandatory if you don't have time. We created this Bible Study Journal with our simple approach to Bible Study so you can go deep into a small portion of Scripture to explore God's Word.

Choosing a Flourish Bible Study Journal is a great first step to strengthening your spiritual muscles a little bit each day. We know you'll grow as you:

1. **Get curious about the Word.** What does the Word say about your situation? What does it say about God himself? About your family? About the future? As you learn more about the Bible, how to study it, and how to dig deeper, you will become hungry to get into the Word.

2. **Get to Know Jesus.** Jesus is the Word personified. He embodies everything God desires to reveal to us. John tells us that *"the Word became flesh and dwelt among us." John 1:14 (ESV)* That's Jesus!

His love and obedience crushed the power of death. By getting to know Him, we come to understand the whole Bible in terms of God's plan to rescue all of humanity–this includes you and me, right here, right now, today.

3. **Seek for a personal word.** When trying to gain understanding, we look for answers in several places. You may reach out to trusted leaders in your life. It is good to seek wisdom in a multitude of counsel, but then you must draw away to a quiet place and seek God yourself with this prayer, *Father, I have sought much advice, and now I want to know what You have to say about this situation.* When we pursue God directly, and the inevitable storms come, the word God has spoken will hold us like an anchor to the Rock.

This is how you flourish in faith, family and life. You dig into the Word, fasten your gaze on the person of Jesus, and wait until you receive a personal word. The DECLARE Bible Study Approach is the key to bringing all these elements together. This less-is-more approach guides you to dig into the Bible and hear Jesus speak.

When we press into God's Word and hear His voice, we gain confidence that He will never fail us. God may be later than expected. He may not answer like we imagined, but He knows what we need. God loves multiplication. This is good news! When pursuing God, you get out MORE than you put into it. Psalm 34:4 says, *"God met me more than halfway."* (MSG) We're thrilled you're here, digging in with us.

A Note to Group Leaders

We are pleased that you have chosen to gather a group of ladies to enjoy this Flourish Bible Study together. The study is designed to create deep, thoughtful conversations. Chatting through the insights gained using the five simple DECLARE practices each week will guide the discussion to reveal personal a-ha's that come straight from Scripture. It is motivating and encouraging when ladies share how God speaks in their lives.

We have provided here a few considerations regarding scheduling:

† Since it is a four-week study, you have several choices for your meeting schedule. You can meet up weekly for four weeks, or maybe you meet only twice and cover two weeks at a time. Most groups enjoy 1-1/2 or 2 hours together.

† Some groups like to add a fifth meeting time to gather before the study begins to hand out the books.

We suggest that you make use of the weekly **Discussion Topics** located at the end of each week to facilitate the discussion. Most facilitators like to use this guide as a building block to create a general time schedule for your meeting. You may want to reserve fifteen minutes or so at the end of your group time to share prayer requests.

Gathering women to share their stories invites God's love to shine: *"They triumphed over him by the blood of the Lamb and by the word of their testimony."* (Revelation 12:11) We pray that you are blessed as you flourish together!

Table of Contents

Reading Plan & Weekly Scripture Declaration

Week 1

Reading Plan:
Judges 6:1-24

Week 1 Declaration:
Proverbs 19:21

"Many are the plans in a person's heart, but it is the Lord's purpose that prevails." (NIV)

Week 2

Reading Plan:
Judges 6:25-40

Week 2 Declaration:
Hebrews 11:1

"Now faith is confidence in what we hope for and assurance about what we do not see." (NIV)

Week 3

Reading Plan:
Judges 7

Week 3 Declaration:
Ephesians 6:10

"Finally, be strong in the Lord and in his mighty power." (NIV)

Week 4

Reading Plan:
Judges 8

Week 4 Declaration:
2 Corinthians 4:7

"But we have this precious treasure, the good news about salvation, in unworthy earthen vessels of human frailty, so that the grandeur and surpassing greatness of the power will be shown to be from God—His sufficiency—and not from ourselves." (AMP)

Declare Bible Study Approach

"We know that the Son of God has come and has given us understanding, so that we may know him who is true. . . ."

1 John 5:20

The Declare Bible Study Approach equips us to dig deeper into a passage of scripture in order to know God's Word intimately and apply it to our lives. *(1 Corinthians 2:10-15)* When His Word is activated in our midst, new life is released, and we will begin to flourish where we are planted.

Learn more about the DECLARE Bible Study Approach and how to use online Bible study aids. Log onto **www.flourishgathering.com/declare** to view our video series.

ENGAGE Prayer Method

The DECLARE Bible Study Approach begins by engaging or tuning your ears and heart to God's voice. The ENGAGE Prayer Method prepares your heart and mind to hear:

TOSS: Throw your cares on God. Let Him bear your burdens. *Psalm 55:22*

CATCH: Receive the peace that surpasses all understanding. *Philippians 4:7*

INVITE: Take every thought captive. Invite clarity and focus. Refuse confusion, distraction, or double-mindedness. *2 Corinthians 10:5*

OPEN: Ask God if you have turned away or closed your heart to anyone. Release the offense, open your heart, and give the situation into God's care. *Psalm 139:23*

EXPECT: Tell God that you are looking forward to hearing from Him. Let the excitement of time in His presence build expectation in your heart. *Habakkuk 2:1*

STAGE 1: *Read & Write* 📖

Start with a verse or short passage that you want to explore further:

† Read the scripture slowly once or twice, even out loud if you are able.

† Write the scripture in your journal, including verses before and after.

† Read the entire chapter for context.

† Read the passage in another translation.

STAGE 2: *Investigate* 🔍

Once you have read the scripture and corresponding chapter, there are several options that you can use to look deeper into the meditation Scripture. Investigate as little or as much as time allows. Online resources like BibleGateway.com or BlueLetterBible.org will help:

† Highlight the words in the meditation verse you want to research more. We teach you how to do a word study to gain greater insight into the passage.

† Read other verses with a similar message, called cross references. Reading cross references will help you better understand a verse, word, or principle.

† Read a commentary.

STAGE 3: *Imagine*

Read the meditation verse and insert yourself in the story. Use your imagination to be present in the scene. Ask yourself the following questions:

†   When and where is this taking place?

†   Who is speaking? About what? Why?

†   What are the characteristics of God as shown through this scripture or chapter?

†   What are the promises of God as shown through this scripture or chapter?

STAGE 4: *Listen*

Invite the Words of Scripture and the Words of God to speak personally into your mind and heart. You can ask these questions:

†   How do these verses apply to me?

†   Is there anything that I need to receive or surrender in my life?

†   Lord, how I can apply Your Word to the frustrations, disappointments, fears, or hurts in my life?

Listening can be pursued for several days, and in fact, God will probably speak unexpectedly at random times of day or night as His revelation is released to you.

STAGE 5: *Declare* 🎙

Write out a declaration of what you have received as you meditated on the Word. This can be a statement of God's promise to you, an affirmation of the healing that He has given you, or a proclamation of a truth that has become real to you. A declaration can include Scripture, your own words, or some of each.

Looking for a Story of Power

I stare at the daunting obstacle, frightened and full of doubt. "I don't think I can," slips out of my mouth.

My mentor replies, "She who says, '*I can't*,' and she who says, '*I can*,'" both speak truth."

At times, life is one relentless slog up a looming mountain. Sure, you find periodic overlooks to enjoy the view, but then it's back to plodding, one heavy foot in front of the other. You hear the whip crack, urging you forward. Or perhaps a carrot dangling before your eyes, luring you to strive for a potential-but-not-promised reward.

Then the trail steepens and narrows. Loose rocks fall from above, and your eyes weep as debris obscures your sight. Pausing to wipe your soiled brow, you cry out. *Oh, God, where are you? Am I on the right path? Is this the glory you called me to? If this is my story, I want out.*

You sit down right in the middle of the path, considering which is worse: heading back down or pushing forward. Now the tears are real. *I can't do this. It's too hard. I've lost my way. I have no idea if you're still listening, Jesus. I want this to end.*

You sense the Lord's reply: *You don't have to do this alone. I want your life to reveal My glory, even in dark and difficult times. You are not alone. You are Mine. Let's do this together.*

Your good Father sits with you, wiping the tears, holding you close. At last, He takes your hand and invites you to stand again. On wobbly legs, you rise and take one small step.

As you walk, supernatural power fills your mind and body. Your "*I can't*" becomes a tentative "*I think I can.*" The persevering strength that sustained Jesus' broken body as He dragged himself up the Holy Mountain to crush the power of death arises in your heart. Your eyes shine with fresh determination as your steps become strong and sure. The path is still steep. Ominous skies threaten. The peak is obscured, but unexpected confidence propels you forward.

I can because God can.

With "*I can*" on your lips, your story of purpose, your story of overcoming is revealed daily in the pages of your life. The obstacles you face may not change, but God changes your view of the obstacles. God equips you with the faith, courage and perseverance you need to take His hand and take the next step.

Yes! So where can I find some of that?

We pondered this question and asked God to highlight whose story in Scripture might encourage and instruct us with the practical *how* to walk this out, *how* to invite Holy Spirit power into our stories. It didn't take long for the Lord to highlight a familiar tale in the book of Judges. As we sat with Gideon, we knew he was our guide.

We find our man Gideon hiding, afraid, trying to make ends meet, to get some food on the table. His life is a daily uphill battle, surrounded by enemies who want to sabotage his livelihood and tear his family apart. He is pressed on every side, wondering why God shirked His promises:

> *"If God is with us, why has all this happened to us?*
> *Where are all the miracle-wonders our parents*
> *and grandparents told us about, telling us, 'Didn't*
> *God deliver us from Egypt?' The fact is, God has*
> *nothing to do with us...."* Judges 6:13 (MSG)

Whoa, don't you appreciate that Gideon hurls with honesty his deepest frustrations and darkest doubts? I'm right there with him, frightened by the steep trail up my looming mountain. *God, where are you? Have you abandoned me? How much longer do I have to endure this trial? This is not the story I signed up for.*

Don't worry. God answers. Let's find out what He says to Gideon, and what He says to you, as we dig into Judges chapters 6-8. We're eager to find faith, courage and perseverance to walk into our story of power, our story of purpose.

WEEK ONE

A Story of Purpose

DECLARATION VERSE

"Many are the plans in a person's heart, but it is the Lord's purpose that prevails." Proverbs 19:21

What's in a Name?

What do you notice when you see yourself in the mirror? Now, be honest. I don't take selfies often, but when I do, it's alarming, *"Is that what I look like?! Goodness, I hope not!"*

You may not disparage your looks—most women are hard on themselves—but that's simply the outward appearance. Going deeper, how do you feel about yourself as a person?

What gives you value?

We all receive mixed messages about our identity influenced by family of origin, culture, opportunities and choices. Your life may have presented many open doors, or perhaps you were forced onto a path by circumstances beyond your control: married, single, divorced, pregnant, childless, career-focused, stay-at-home, university educated, self-taught.

The conditions of your life create labels, some given by others and some chosen by yourself. What labels do you wear? I don't know the obstacles you're facing, the concerns plaguing your mind, the fears wearying your heart. But I'm certain you desire to live with a sense of purpose. God made us that way. Unfortunately, the forces of the world seek to sabotage our sense of purpose, distracting us with confusion and disillusionment.

We fight a daily battle to keep our eyes on the path, ears tuned to Holy Spirit, and thoughts filled with truth, especially when circumstances oppose our expectations. Just like Gideon, one of God's chosen people during a not-so-glorious time when the nation suffered under foreign oppressors who ravaged the land, leaving the Hebrews to starve. We meet Gideon taking cover in a winepress trying to thresh wheat undetected. He is in survival mode—dejected and afraid—part of the weakest clan and a nobody in his own family. (Judges 6:15)

Imagine Gideon's shock when he is addressed as a "mighty warrior." *Who, me? You've got to be kidding! That'll be the day.*

Why is it so hard to let God give us a new name? When we believe in Christ, God sees us as a new creation, cleansed by His redeeming blood shed at Calvary. The old is gone. The new is here. God has prepared a life of purpose for you in Christ Jesus, but those old labels get in the way. Can you hear Gideon's doubt? *Mighty warrior indeed! What a joke.*

If we allow our present reality to limit our faith, our new name will sound absurd. We cling to our familiar identity and stay in our habitual patterns, hiding in that winepress. Gideon doubts his new name because it contradicts the reality he perceives with his natural eyes: *I don't see any wonders or miracles. We are oppressed by powerful enemies. God is nowhere to be seen, and now I'm being asked to save Israel? That's absurd. With what resources? Have you noticed— we're starving?*

Gideon is in survival mode. His plan is to hide away and stay alive. Hope for a glorious future is nonexistent. His lofty aspiration is to secure enough food so his family doesn't perish. That's it. Lack of resources is soul crushing. When we focus on what we don't have, we are blinded to a story of purpose in our lives.

I'm not young enough, old enough, rich enough, beautiful enough, smart enough, or powerful enough. Since when are those prerequisites to an overcoming life? In 1 Corinthians 3, Paul tells us that the wisdom of the world is foolishness to Christ. God's ways are not our ways. Weakness overcomes strength. Miracles transform lack into plenty; a few crumbs of food feed thousands. Jesus chooses twelve unlikely recruits to walk with him for three short years, and they alter the course of history. The numbers don't add up—the statistics don't make sense.

Without Holy Spirit inspiration, we cannot comprehend God's ways. We lack the capacity to dream big. We settle for less, diminished by our old names that write small, safe, survival stories for our lives. I get Gideon. I've been there, holding tight to the hope that I'll survive the day, my aspirations dashed on the rocks of failure and disappointment. *Where are you God? You have abandoned me.*

But Jesus calls us higher, draws our gaze to heaven, and inspires us with the potential that resides in every life, in every story. **He longs to ignite a sense of purpose that makes our story His Story.** Some days we dream too small and lose hope. Some days we dream too big and feel overwhelmed:

> *"Many are the plans in a person's heart, but it is the Lord's purpose that prevails."* Proverbs 19:21

We have many plans that vacillate with changing circumstances, influenced by our mood, finances, news, weather, and random input we receive from a thousand sources each day. Without a Holy Spirit anchor, our human nature shifts with every changing current. Even worse are the storms that shake us until we're nauseous, ready to throw overboard all our plans in exchange for relief.

Life offers struggles, but God offers purpose. He gives you a new name as evidence of your calling. His Word stands true and strong despite circumstances that may shake us to the core. Jesus has an eternal perspective—He does not lose hope. When we yield our heart to His larger purpose and turn away from our smaller schemes, we position ourselves to become participants in His Story. We become conduits of His love, the most powerful force in the universe.

But can we trust His love? Is this all-powerful God approachable? At times, He is intimidating, evoking fear in those who encounter the mighty Yahweh. When Gideon realizes he is conversing with God, our warrior shudders in fear, but the Lord reassures him with a blessing of peace.

God imparts supernatural confidence to Gideon, and He does the same for us, empowering us to survive and even thrive in any challenge we face. ***He intends to equip us with the faith, courage, and perseverance needed to walk into our story of purpose.*** He reassures our desperate, doubting soul with His peace. His shalom restores to us a sound mind and heart.

After Gideon encounters the living God, he builds an altar and brings a sacrifice. He creates a place of worship, a place of remembrance, a sanctuary he will return to when the pressure of his "mighty warrior" calling becomes more than he can bear. May you find such a place to meet with God when you need to hear Him whisper your true name and remind you of the powerful story He is writing with your life.

Mindy

ENGAGE Prayer Method

The DECLARE Bible Study Approach begins by engaging or tuning your ears and heart to God's voice. The ENGAGE Prayer Method prepares your heart and mind to hear:

TOSS: Throw your cares on God. Let Him bear your burdens. *Psalm 55:22*

CATCH: Receive the peace that surpasses all understanding. *Philippians 4:7*

INVITE: Take every thought captive. Invite clarity and focus. Refuse confusion, distraction, or double-mindedness. *2 Corinthians 10:5*

OPEN: Ask God if you have turned away or closed your heart to anyone. Release the offense, open your heart, and give the situation into God's care. *Psalm 139:23*

EXPECT: Tell God that you are looking forward to hearing from Him. Let the excitement of time in His presence build expectation in your heart. *Habakkuk 2:1*

Declaration Verse
"Many are the plans in a person's
heart, but it is the Lord's
purpose that prevails."
Proverbs 19:21

DAY ONE

TODAY'S DECLARE PRACTICE *Read & Write*

[ ] Read Proverbs 19:21 slowly once or twice, even out loud if
you are able.

[ ] Write Proverbs 19:20-22 in the space below. *Feel free to
get creative!*

_____

_____

_____

_____

_____

_____

HAVE A LITTLE MORE TIME?

[ ] Read Proverbs chapter 19 for context.
Write out a few observations.

_____

_____

_____

_____

_____

_____

_____

_____

_____

_____

[ ] Read Proverbs 19:21 in another Bible translation.
Do you notice any differences?

Write your observations.

_____

_____

_____

_____

_____

_____

_____

_____

_____

_____

🌱 DIGGING DEEPER: JUDGES 6:1-24

[ ] Read Judges 6:1-24

[ ] Read and Write

Write any verse that stands out to you.

_____

_____

_____

_____

_____

_____

_____

_____

_____

_____

_____

_____

_____

[ ] Write down any general thoughts or questions you have as you read the passage today.

_____

_____

_____

_____

_____

_____

_____

_____

_____

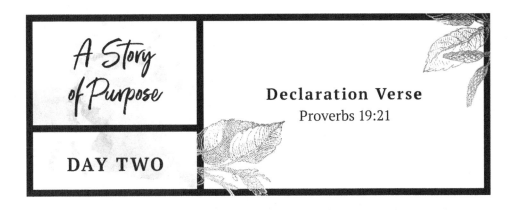

A Story of Purpose

Declaration Verse
Proverbs 19:21

DAY TWO

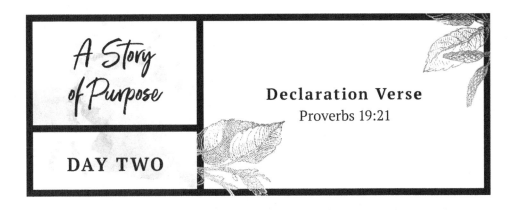 **TODAY'S DECLARE PRACTICE** *Investigate* 🔍

Today we begin looking deeper into the Declaration Verse. Investigate as little or as much as time allows. Online resources like BibleGateway.com or BlueLetterBible.org will help you during your investigation.

[ ] Conduct a Word Study: Part One

Read the Declaration Verse. Highlighting any words you want to research more. Write these words below.

_____

_____

_____

_____

[ ] Conduct a Word Study: Part Two

Want to learn more about the DECLARE Bible Study
Approach and how to do a word study? Log onto
www.flourishgathering.com/declare to view our
video series.

Using BlueLetterBible.org or another online resource,
choose a word you selected above to conduct your word
study. This is as simple as looking up the original Greek
or Hebrew word, reading the definitions of that word,
and looking at how it is used in other verses in the Bible.

Record the results of your word study here.

HAVE A LITTLE MORE TIME?

[ ] Read any of the following cross references for Proverbs 19:21:

† Hebrews 6:17

† Psalm 33:11

† Isaiah 46:10

Reading cross references will help you better understand a verse, word, or principle. What did you discover? Write your insights.

_____

_____

_____

_____

_____

_____

_____

_____

_____

_____

_____

[ ] Read a commentary. A commentary is a collection of
explanatory notes that a Bible scholar has written about
scripture. You can find these online. A good place to begin
is Matthew Henry, C.H. Spurgeon, or David Guzik.

Write any observations, quotes, or notes.

_____

_____

_____

_____

_____

_____

_____

_____

_____

_____

_____

_____

_____

_____

DIGGING DEEPER: JUDGES 6:1-24

[ ] Read Judges 6:1-24

[ ] Investigate

Highlight a couple of key words that stand out to you in the verses you read. Using BlueLetterBible.org look up the Greek or Hebrew word and definition of one of those words. Write your findings below.

_____

_____

_____

_____

_____

_____

_____

_____

_____

_____

[ ] Write down any general thoughts or questions you have as
you read the verses today.

_____

_____

_____

_____

_____

_____

_____

_____

_____

_____

_____

_____

_____

_____

A Story
of Purpose

DAY THREE

Reading Passage
Judges 6:1-24

TODAY'S DECLARE PRACTICE *Imagine*

Remember to ENGAGE as you prepare to imagine: toss, catch, invite, open, expect. Invite the Words of Scripture and the Words of God to speak personally into your mind and heart.

[ ] Read Judges 6:1-24

You may want to read different translations. We suggest you scout around in your Bible for any notes on the book of Judges or specifically the life of Gideon. When using your imagination, it helps to keep in mind the context of the chapter and book that you're in. Insert yourself in the scene as you ponder the following questions. Use your imagination and all your senses to be present in the words of Scripture.

[ ] When and where is this taking place? What do you
    imagine you might see, hear, touch, taste, or smell?

_____

_____

_____

_____

_____

_____

_____

_____

[ ] Why are we introduced to Gideon in the winepress?
    What is he doing there?

_____

_____

_____

_____

_____

_____

_____

_____

_____

_____

_____

_____

_____

_____

[ ] Put yourself in Gideon's shoes as he engages with God.
     Why does Gideon act as he does? Why does he build an altar?

_____

_____

_____

_____

_____

_____

_____

_____

_____

_____

_____

_____

_____

_____

HAVE A LITTLE MORE TIME?

[ ] What are the characteristics of God shown in Judges 6:1-24?

Is He steadfast, faithful, just, trustworthy, nurturing, kind, gentle, or strong? What do you see revealed about His nature in these verses?

_____

_____

_____

_____

_____

_____

_____

_____

_____

_____

_____

_____

_____

_____

[ ] What are the promises of God as shown through the reading?

Write any observations, key words, or questions you have as you ponder the reading passage. If you have time, you may want to do another word study.

_____

_____

_____

_____

_____

_____

_____

_____

_____

DIGGING DEEPER: PROVERBS 19:21

[ ] Read Proverbs 19:21

[ ] Imagine

Why did God inspire Solomon to write this proverb?
What challenges in life does this wisdom address?

_____

_____

_____

_____

_____

_____

_____

_____

_____

_____

_____

_____

[ ] Do you have many plans? How can you let the Lord's
    purpose prevail?

_____

_____

_____

_____

_____

_____

_____

_____

_____

_____

_____

_____

_____

_____

_____

_____

A Story
of Purpose

DAY FOUR

Reading Passage
Judges 6:1-24

TODAY'S DECLARE PRACTICE *Listen* 🎧

> *Remember to take a moment to ENGAGE as you prepare*
> *to listen: toss, catch, invite, open, expect. Invite the Words*
> *of Scripture and the Words of God to speak personally into*
> *your mind and heart. Remember that God's voice will never*
> *accuse you. He may bring gentle conviction, and that can*
> *cause some grief, but God always brings hope.*

Listening can be pursued for several days, and in fact,
God will probably speak unexpectedly at random times
of day or night as His revelation is released to you.
Ask these questions as you listen to God's voice.

[ ] How do these events in Gideon's life apply to me?
What do you want me to see, God?

_____

_____

_____

_____

_____

_____

_____

🌱 HAVE A LITTLE MORE TIME?

[ ] Ponder and pray: how I can apply this part of Gideon's
story to the frustrations, disappointments, fears, or hurts
in my life? Is there anything I need to surrender or receive
in my life?

_____

_____

_____

_____

_____

_____

_____

_____

_____

_____

_____

_____

🌿 DIGGING DEEPER: PROVERBS 19:21

[ ] Read Proverbs 19:21

[ ] Listen

Ask yourself: how do the truths I find in this verse apply
to me? What does God want to say?

_____

_____

_____

_____

_____

_____

_____

_____

_____

_____

_____

_____

_____

_____

[ ] Think of a difficult situation you're facing right now.
     What does the Declaration Verse speak to your heart?

_____

_____

_____

_____

_____

_____

_____

_____

_____

_____

_____

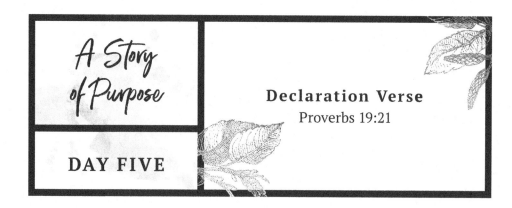

A Story of Purpose

Declaration Verse
Proverbs 19:21

DAY FIVE

 TODAY'S DECLARE PRACTICE *Declare*

Write out a declaration of what you received as you
meditated on the Word. This can be a statement of God's
promise to you, an affirmation of the healing He has given
you, or a proclamation of a truth that has become real to
you. A declaration can include Scripture, your own words,
or some of each.

_____

_____

_____

_____

_____

_____

_____

_____

_____

_____

_____

_____

_____

_____

_____

_____

_____

REFLECT ON YOUR WEEK

Write out Proverbs 19:21 by hand if you memorized it or summarize the Declaration Verse in your own words below.

_____

_____

_____

_____

_____

_____

_____

_____

_____

_____

_____

_____

_____

_____

Spend a few minutes documenting your insights, "a-ha" moments, and revelations from this week of digging into the Bible.

_____

_____

_____

_____

_____

_____

_____

Week One: Discussion Topics

We provide discussion topics to help facilitate conversations with friends as you enjoy this study together, or you can ponder these questions as a personal reflection. Even if you are not able to meet up with others, you're invited to join us in our private Facebook Group at facebook.com/groups/flourishgathering/

1. Do you have any thoughts or reactions to this week's devotional? Here are two passages to inspire conversation:

   "The conditions of your life create labels, some given by others and some chosen by yourself. What labels do you wear?" (page 18)

   "When we focus on what we don't have, we are blinded to a story of purpose in our lives. I'm not young enough, old enough, rich enough, beautiful enough, smart enough, or powerful enough. Since when are those prerequisites to an overcoming life?" (page 19)

2. Was there a special insight you gained from the **Investigate** practice? Perhaps an interesting word study, cross reference, or commentary?

3. What happened when you used your **Imagination**? What did you discover about the context of this chapter or book of the Bible? If you had time, did you gain insight into the character or promises of God?

4. Did God speak something special that you would like to share as you **Listened**?

5. What is your **Declaration**? How can we pray for you in this regard?

6. How can we support one another this week? Prayer requests? Praise reports?

Notes

_____

_____

_____

_____

_____

_____

_____

_____

_____

_____

_____

_____

_____

_____

WEEK TWO

A Story of Faith

DECLARATION VERSE

"Now faith is confidence in what we hope for and assurance about what we do not see." Hebrews 11:1

Hold Fast with Confidence

My husband's voice came through the phone, *"Mindy, it's worse than we imagined. Much worse. Can you talk?"*

As I processed the unfolding events, my reeling mind and emotions searched for solid footing. I recalled my usual morning prayer: *Father, I don't yet know what today holds, but you do. This day may be one to enjoy, or it might be one to endure, but through it all, your mercies are new every morning. Help me trust you. I want to flourish no matter what this day reveals.*

This prayer reminds me that God is sovereign. No matter what events shake my world, when I hold fast to His love and purpose, His grace works all things for good. (Romans 8:28) When I'm blindsided by news too shocking to believe, this prayer anchors me in the storm.

During trials, we usually have one of two responses: either we hide and wait for the storm to pass, or we act and get to work finding a solution. I remember the first time God told me, *"I will fight for you; you need only to be still." (Exodus 14:14)*

It had to be the Lord because those words do not naturally enter my mind. My usual response is to start problem solving and make a plan, but I have learned the value of waiting and watching to see what God is doing.

I'm right there with Gideon, hiding in the winepress, waiting for the storm to clear. The Israelites have been crying out for relief for seven long years. God has answered through a prophet, urging them to turn away from false gods, but they are unwilling. The Israelites will not find freedom until they stop worshipping Baal, but this means upsetting the status quo. In their pain, they have found respite in false gods. No one is bold enough to destroy the places of idol worship and risk community outrage.

How many times have I been there, on the fence, unwilling to confront my lukewarm faith and reject the idolatry of my heart? *I'm yours God, but I also enjoy these comforts. Can't I have a little bit of both? Don't make me choose.* But God is clear that we must choose. We will struggle to walk in His power if our heart is divided.

When God instructs Gideon to confront the status quo by tearing down Baal altars and Asherah poles, our crusader obeys, but he uses the cover of night to hide. He knows these actions will ignite a hostile backlash. The secret isn't a secret for long, and the rumor mill identifies Gideon as the perpetrator.

How does Gideon find the inner strength to take this bold and unpopular stand? *When I am called, will I be able to do the same?* **Courageous obedience begins with faith.** When we trust God's Word and stand with confidence in His strength, we can step out with assurance.

*"Now faith is confidence in what we hope for and
assurance about what we do not see."* Hebrews 11:1

What do you hope for? What do you not yet see? Hebrews chapter 11 recounts the lives of women and men who lived in courageous obedience. They were not promised comfort and ease; in fact, some of their stories are downright terrifying, **but they found their safe place in God's will.**

Faith in God is the empowering force that leads us into a life of purpose. Without it, we cannot please God, so how do we cultivate a strong faith? Hebrews chapter 12 provides insight into the how: *"Therefore, since we are surrounded by such a great cloud of witnesses, let us throw off everything that hinders and the sin that so easily entangles. And let us run with perseverance the race marked out for us, fixing our eyes on Jesus, the pioneer and perfecter of faith."* Hebrews 12:1-2a

Gospel basics: turn from sin and run to Jesus! We don't need to complicate our faith. The message is simple—don't let sin get a foothold and stay connected to Jesus. *OK, sounds reasonable, but why is it so hard to do?* As I've pondered this question, I see four main ways the enemy attacks our faith and gets our eyes off Jesus.

I doubt God. *Is He good? Is He powerful to save? Does He care what's happening to me?* Doubt makes God seem small and irrelevant. It fights against faith like a virus that gets into my thoughts and spreads fear. (Psalm 27) Just as Gideon put out the fleece (twice!), we strengthen our faith when we ask God to confirm His word and create a quiet space to listen.

I doubt myself. *Do I have what it takes? The task is too difficult.* When I set my eyes on myself rather than Jesus, I worry about my weakness. I forget that my weakness creates space for God's power to show up. All you need is a mustard-seed faith that turns to God for help. When you admit your lack, God releases His plenty. (2 Corinthians 12:9)

I look at the circumstances. Yes, we are surrounded by challenges. Yes, Satan is on the prowl. Yes, scary stuff happens. Even in Hebrews 11, our heroes of faith suffered as they obeyed God's call on their lives, but they overcame evil with good. Jesus tells us straight: we will face trouble, but when we keep our eyes on Him, we will overcome. (John 16:33)

I look at my past failure. *How can the Lord use me when I have been so faithless? Look at my litany of royal blunders.* When we meet Gideon, he does not resemble the "mighty warrior" he will become. If he continued to look at the past instead of acting on God's call, he would have missed the miracle. Looking forward, we tune our ears to the cheers of the great cloud of witnesses and fix our eyes on Jesus who speaks into being that which does not yet exist. (Psalm 33)

Jesus desires to be the author and finisher of your faith (Hebrews 12:2), but you get to choose. Faith and fear fight for your attention. Doubt attacks confidence. We keep our eyes on Jesus, so when that phone call brings bad news, we hold fast by faith with confidence in God. Your life may be shaken, but you won't be crushed when He is your cornerstone. God wants to write your story of faith, courage and perseverance as you experience His power released in your life.

Mindy

ENGAGE Prayer Method

The DECLARE Bible Study Approach begins by engaging or tuning your ears and heart to God's voice. The ENGAGE Prayer Method prepares your heart and mind to hear:

TOSS: Throw your cares on God. Let Him bear your burdens. *Psalm 55:22*

CATCH: Receive the peace that surpasses all understanding. *Philippians 4:7*

INVITE: Take every thought captive. Invite clarity and focus. Refuse confusion, distraction, or double-mindedness. *2 Corinthians 10:5*

OPEN: Ask God if you have turned away or closed your heart to anyone. Release the offense, open your heart, and give the situation into God's care. *Psalm 139:23*

EXPECT: Tell God that you are looking forward to hearing from Him. Let the excitement of time in His presence build expectation in your heart. *Habakkuk 2:1*

A Story of Faith

DAY ONE

Declaration Verse
"Now faith is confidence in what we hope for and assurance about what we do not see."
Hebrews 11:1

 TODAY'S DECLARE PRACTICE *Read & Write*

[ ] Read Hebrews 11:1 slowly once or twice, even out loud if you are able.

[ ] Write Hebrews 10:39-11:2 in the space below. *Feel free to get creative!*

_____

_____

_____

_____

_____

_____

_____

_____

HAVE A LITTLE MORE TIME?

[ ] Read Hebrews chapters 11-12 for context. Write out a few observations.

_____

_____

_____

_____

_____

_____

[ ] Read Hebrews 11:1 in another Bible translation.
Do you notice any differences?

Write your observations.

_____

_____

_____

_____

_____

_____

DIGGING DEEPER: JUDGES 6:25-40

[ ] Read Judges 6:25-40

[ ] Read and Write

Write any verse that stands out to you as you read this passage.

_____

_____

_____

_____

_____

[ ] Write down any general thoughts or questions you have as
you read these verses.

_____

_____

_____

_____

_____

_____

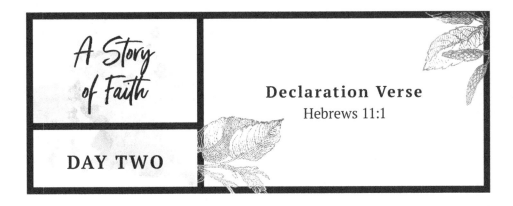

A Story of Faith

Declaration Verse
Hebrews 11:1

DAY TWO

🌿 **TODAY'S DECLARE PRACTICE** *Investigate* 🔍

Today we begin looking deeper into the Declaration Verse. Investigate as little or as much as time allows. Online resources like BibleGateway.com or BlueLetterBible.org will help you during your investigation.

[ ] Conduct a Word Study: Part One

Read the Declaration Verse. Spend a few minutes highlighting any words you want to research more. Write these words below.

_____

_____

_____

_____

_____

_____

_____

_____

_____

_____

[ ] Conduct a Word Study: Part Two

Using BlueLetterBible.org or another online resource, choose a word you selected above to conduct your word study. This is as simple as looking up the original Greek or Hebrew word, reading the definitions of that word, and looking at how it is used in other verses in the Bible.

Record the results of your word study here.

_____

_____

_____

_____

_____

_____

_____

HAVE A LITTLE MORE TIME?

[ ] Read any of the following cross references for Hebrews 11:1:

†   Romans 8:24

†   2 Corinthians 4:18

†   1 Thessalonians 5:8

Reading cross references will help you better understand a verse, word, or principle.

What did you discover? Write your insights:

_____

_____

_____

_____

_____

_____

_____

[ ] Read a commentary. A commentary is a collection of explanatory notes that a Bible scholar has written about scripture. You can find these online. A good place to begin is Matthew Henry, C.H. Spurgeon, or David Guzik.

Write any observations, quotes, or notes.

_____

_____

_____

_____

_____

_____

_____

_____

DIGGING DEEPER: JUDGES 6:25-40

[ ] Read Judges 6:25-40

[ ] Investigate

Highlight a couple of key words that stand out to you in the verses you read. Using BlueLetterBible.org look up the Greek or Hebrew word and definition of one of those words.

Write your findings below.

_____

_____

_____

_____

_____

_____

_____

_____

_____

_____

_____

_____

[ ] Write down any general thoughts or questions you have as
you read the verses today.

_____

_____

_____

_____

_____

_____

_____

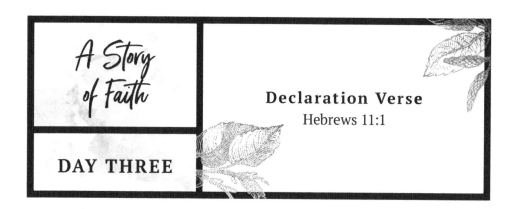

A Story of Faith

Declaration Verse
Hebrews 11:1

DAY THREE

 TODAY'S DECLARE PRACTICE *Imagine*

Remember to ENGAGE as you prepare to imagine: toss, catch, invite, open, expect. Invite the Words of Scripture and the Words of God to speak personally into your mind and heart.

[ ] Read Hebrews chapter 11

Use your imagination and all your senses to be present in the scene.

[ ] How does faith provide confidence?

_____

_____

_____

_____

_____

_____

_____

[ ] What "faith substitutes" do you reach for to create confidence or assurance in your heart? Perhaps education, money, power, or....?

_____

_____

_____

_____

_____

_____

[ ] How would more faith in God help you to have certainty or peace about what you don't yet see?

_____

_____

_____

_____

_____

_____

_____

_____

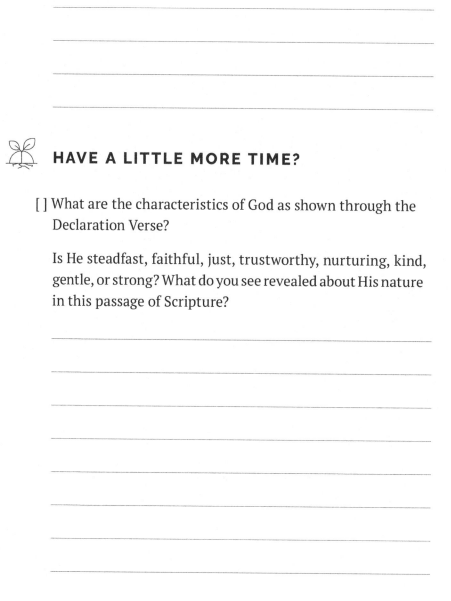 **HAVE A LITTLE MORE TIME?**

[ ] What are the characteristics of God as shown through the Declaration Verse?

Is He steadfast, faithful, just, trustworthy, nurturing, kind, gentle, or strong? What do you see revealed about His nature in this passage of Scripture?

_____

_____

_____

_____

_____

_____

_____

_____

[ ] What promises of God are revealed through the
Declaration Verse?

Write any observations, key words, or questions you have
as you ponder the Declaration Verse. If you have time, you
may want to do another word study.

_____

_____

_____

_____

_____

_____

_____

_____

DIGGING DEEPER JUDGES 6:25-40

[ ] Read Judges 6:25-40

[ ] Imagine

Insert yourself in the scene. Imagine you are there in the
Bible story. What is happening? What do you notice?

_____

_____

_____

_____

_____

_____

_____

_____

_____

_____

[ ] Write down any general thoughts or questions you have as you read the verses today.

_____

_____

_____

_____

_____

_____

_____

_____

_____

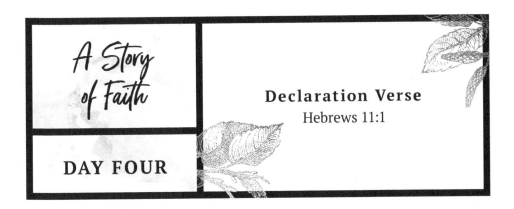

A Story of Faith

Declaration Verse
Hebrews 11:1

DAY FOUR

 TODAY'S DECLARE PRACTICE *Listen*

Remember to take a moment to ENGAGE as you prepare to listen: toss, catch, invite, open, expect. Invite the Words of Scripture and the Words of God to speak personally into your mind and heart. Remember that God's voice will never accuse you. He may bring gentle conviction, and that can cause some grief, but God always brings hope.

Listening can be pursued for several days, and in fact, God will probably speak unexpectedly at random times of day or night as His revelation is released to you. Ask these questions as you listen to God's voice:

[ ] How does this verse apply to me?

_____

_____

_____

_____

_____

_____

_____

_____

_____

_____

_____

_____

🌱 HAVE A LITTLE MORE TIME?

[ ] Ponder and pray: God, please show me how I seek assurance in times of trouble. Are you strong enough to protect
me instead? Am I safe to hope in you?

_____

_____

_____

_____

DIGGING DEEPER: JUDGES 6:25-40

[ ] Read Judges 6:25-40

[ ] Listen

Ask yourself: how does this part of Gideon's life apply to me? What does God want to speak to my heart today through these truths?

_____

_____

_____

_____

_____

_____

_____

[ ] Write down any general thoughts or questions you have as
you read the verses today.

_____

_____

_____

_____

_____

_____

_____

_____

_____

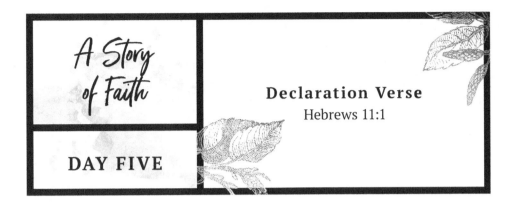

A Story of Faith

DAY FIVE

Declaration Verse
Hebrews 11:1

 TODAY'S DECLARE PRACTICE *Declare*

Write out a declaration of what you have received as you
meditated on the Word. This can be a statement of God's
promise to you, an affirmation of the healing that He has
given you, or a proclamation of a truth that has become
real to you. A declaration can include Scripture, your own
words, or some of each.

_____

_____

_____

_____

_____

_____

REFLECT ON YOUR WEEK

Write out Hebrews 11:1 by hand if you memorized it or summarize the Declaration Verse in your own words below.

Spend a few minutes documenting your insights, "a-ha" moments, and revelations from this week of digging into the Bible.

Week Two: Discussion Topics

We provide discussion topics to help facilitate conversations with friends as you enjoy this study together, or you can ponder these questions as a personal reflection. Even if you are not able to meet up with others, you're invited to join us in our private Facebook Group at facebook.com/groups/flourishgathering/

1. Do you have any thoughts or reactions to this week's devotional? Here are two passages to inspire conversation:

   "During trials, we usually have one of two responses: either we hide and wait for the storm to pass, or we take action and get to work finding a solution. Which is your default?" (page 53)

   "I see four main ways the enemy attacks our faith and gets our eyes off Jesus. Do you recognize any of these in your life? I doubt God. I doubt myself. I look at the circumstances. I look at my past failure." (page 55-56)

2. Was there a special insight you gained from the **Investigate** practice? Perhaps an interesting word study, cross reference, or commentary?

3. What happened when you used your **Imagination**?
    What did you discover about the context of this
    chapter or book of the Bible? If you had time,
    did you gain insight into the character or promises
    of God?

4. Did God speak something special that you would
    like to share as you **Listened**?

5. What is your **Declaration**? How can we pray for
    you in this regard?

6. How can we support one another this week?
    Prayer requests? Praise reports?

Notes

_____

_____

_____

_____

_____

_____

_____

_____

_____

_____

_____

_____

_____

_____

_____

_____

_____

WEEK THREE

A Story of Courage

DECLARATION VERSE

"Finally, be strong in the Lord and in his mighty power." Ephesians 6:10 (NIV)

God Sees You Through

Do you hear the crowd cheering wildly "Gideon, Gideon, Gideon"!

At record speed, Gideon makes his way through the winding wingnut alley, the steep salmon ladder, and the treacherous hourglass drop. Finally, he's arrived at the coveted 14-foot warped wall. Without skipping a beat, and with laser-like precision, he ascends the warped wall and defeats this challenge with courage and strength.

The crowd goes wild.

When I read about the life of Gideon, I see this hero of the faith embodying strength and courage. I imagine him competing in one of my daughter's favorite TV shows, *American Ninja Warrior*. Can you imagine the lineup of strong men and women of the faith competing in Israel's version of this popular competition? That would make for some fun reality TV.

As a culture, we view strength as the quality of being physically strong and able to withstand great force or pressure. We envision bodybuilders and athletes when we think of physical strength. Gideon was likely physically strong as we find him in a winepress threshing wheat, no easy task. Yet, in Judges Chapter 7, we discover that God has a new plan up his sleeve to determine what Gideon is truly made of. Is it just brute strength or strength of character?

In the previous chapter, Gideon strikes down Baal and a nasty civil war ensues. Gideon gathers an army of 32,000 men together to fight the Midianites and a few other tribes. Gideon must feel confident at this point. God has assured him—several times—that through His hand they will be victorious, and there is strength in numbers, right? He's got both!

This is when God interjects, *"Not so fast, my child."* Through a series of tests, the Lord asks Gideon to reduce his army from 32,000 men to only 300. Ouch!

I can imagine how Gideon feels. I've been there. I may not have been going to war, but I've often gone to battle with my plans, remedies and checklists at the ready. So, what is God up to? Why this drastic request? Is God setting Gideon up to fail?

Remember back when Gideon was alone in the winepress, questioning the angel of the Lord? We learn that he was the *"least in his Father's household." (Judges 6:15)* He doubts the calling and questions his qualifications. However, despite Gideon's fears and insecurities, he chooses to obey the Lord's commands. This proves to be the "secret sauce" Gideon needs to see the power of God revealed in this epic story unfolding through the pages of Judges chapter 7.

Self-sufficiency is a handicap which causes us to rely in our own strength. When God strips us of our self-reliance, it forces us to place our full confidence in God and not in ourselves. It builds our strength, not by physical or even mental abilities, but in the Lord, helping us to believe that through His mighty power we can overcome anything. God wants Gideon to know without a shadow of a doubt that although he has anointed, prepared and equipped Gideon, it is by God's grace, power, and strength that the battle is won.

> *"Finally, be strong in the Lord and in his mighty power."* Ephesians 6:10

I always wondered what it meant to be "strong in the Lord." You see, I viewed strength by physical and mental abilities for the task at hand; however, as I read the account of Gideon defeating the Midianites, I discovered that strength has nothing to do with physical abilities or the size of your army. ***Godly strength comes from confidence in who God is and surrender to His power, not ours.***

However, we cannot be "strong in the Lord" without obedience. God calls us, anoints us, prepares us, equips us and promises to walk with us. Our job is to choose to walk forward in faith. That is what we see Gideon do throughout this story in Judges chapter 7. He surrenders his assurance of a strong and mighty army for the only assurance that matters: victory depends not in strength or numbers, but in obedience and commitment to the Lord.

Gideon exudes not only strength of character but also courage of heart. *What does it mean to be courageous?* I consider many heroes of faith, such as Moses, Joseph, David, Esther and Paul, to be courageous. Yet, was it courage or confidence they demonstrated? Each of these mighty men and women had doubts, fears, and crippling insecurities; however, they chose to place their confidence in the mighty power of God rather than their own strengths and abilities.

What battle are you facing today? You may feel neither confident nor courageous. The battles we face in life often leave us feeling discouraged and deflated. Be encouraged by the stories of ordinary men and women who through obedience to the Lord, chose to place their faith and trust in God. Victory may look different for each of us. No matter how great the odds against us may be, our faithful God is sovereign, and He will always see us through the battles we face in life.

ENGAGE Prayer Method

The DECLARE Bible Study Approach begins by engaging or tuning your ears and heart to God's voice. The ENGAGE Prayer Method prepares your heart and mind to hear:

TOSS: Throw your cares on God. Let Him bear your burdens. *Psalm 55:22*

CATCH: Receive the peace that surpasses all understanding. *Philippians 4:7*

INVITE: Take every thought captive. Invite clarity and focus. Refuse confusion, distraction, or double-mindedness. *2 Corinthians 10:5*

OPEN: Ask God if you have turned away or closed your heart to anyone. Release the offense, open your heart, and give the situation into God's care. *Psalm 139:23*

EXPECT: Tell God that you are looking forward to hearing from Him. Let the excitement of time in His presence build expectation in your heart. *Habakkuk 2:1*

A Story of Courage

DAY ONE

Declaration Verse

"Finally, be strong in the Lord and
in his mighty power."
Ephesians 6:10

TODAY'S DECLARE PRACTICE *Read & Write*

[ ] Read Ephesians 6:10 slowly once or twice, even out loud if
you are able.

[ ] Write Ephesians 6:9-11 in the space below. *Feel free to get
creative!*

_____

_____

_____

_____

_____

_____

_____

_____

HAVE A LITTLE MORE TIME?

[ ] Read Ephesians chapter 6 for context.
Write out a few observations.

_____

_____

_____

_____

_____

_____

_____

[ ] Read Ephesians 6:10 in another Bible translation.
Do you notice any differences? Write your observations.

_____

_____

_____

_____

_____

_____

_____

DIGGING DEEPER: JUDGES 7

[ ] Read Judges chapter 7

[ ] Read and Write

Write any verse that stands out to you as you read the
passage.

_____

_____

_____

_____

_____

[ ] Write down any general thoughts or questions you have as
you read these verses.

_____

_____

_____

_____

_____

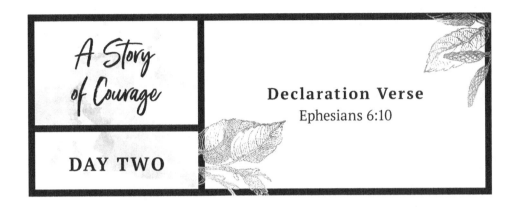

A Story of Courage

DAY TWO

Declaration Verse
Ephesians 6:10

 TODAY'S DECLARE PRACTICE *Investigate*

Today we begin looking deeper into the Declaration Verse.
Investigate as little or as much as time allows. Online
resources like BibleGateway.com or BlueLetterBible.org
will help you during your investigation.

[ ] Conduct a Word Study: Part One

Read the Declaration Verse. Spend a few minutes highlighting any words you want to research more. Write these
words below.

_____

_____

_____

_____

_____

_____

_____

_____

_____

[ ] Conduct a Word Study: Part Two

Using BlueLetterBible.org or another online resource, choose a word you selected above to conduct your word study. This is as simple as looking up the original Greek or Hebrew word, reading the definitions of that word, and looking at how it is used in other verses in the Bible.

Record the results of your word study here:

_____

_____

_____

_____

_____

_____

_____

_____

HAVE A LITTLE MORE TIME?

[ ] Read any of the following cross references for Ephesians 6:10:

  †   I Corinthians 16:13

  †   I Peter 4:11

  †   Ephesians 3:16

Reading cross references will help you better understand a verse, word, or principle.

What did you discover? Write your insights.

_____

_____

_____

_____

_____

_____

_____

[ ] Read a commentary. A commentary is a collection of explanatory notes that a Bible scholar has written about scripture. You can find these online. A good place to begin is Matthew Henry, C.H. Spurgeon, or David Guzik.

Write any observations, quotes, or notes.

_____

_____

_____

_____

_____

_____

_____

_____

🌱 DIGGING DEEPER: JUDGES 7

[ ] Read Judges chapter 7

[ ] Investigate

Highlight a couple of key words that stand out to you in the verses you read. Using BlueLetterBible.org look up the Greek or Hebrew word and definition of one of those words.

Write your findings below.

_____

_____

_____

_____

_____

_____

_____

_____

_____

_____

_____

[ ] Write down any general thoughts or questions you have as
you read the verses today.

_____

_____

_____

_____

_____

_____

_____

_____

_____

_____

A Story
of Courage

DAY THREE

Reading Passage
Judges chapter 7

 TODAY'S DECLARE PRACTICE *Imagine*

Remember to ENGAGE as you prepare to imagine: toss, catch, invite, open, expect. Invite the Words of Scripture and the Words of God to speak personally into your mind and heart.

[ ] Read Judges chapter 7

Use your imagination and all your senses to be present in the scene.

[ ] When and where is this taking place? What do you imagine you might see, hear, touch, taste, or smell?

_____

_____

_____

_____

_____

_____

_____

_____

_____

_____

[ ] What do you think Gideon is feeling as God reduces the
size of his army?

_____

_____

_____

_____

_____

_____

_____

[ ] Have you been encouraged by a dream like Gideon was?

_____

_____

_____

_____

_____

_____

_____

HAVE A LITTLE MORE TIME?

[ ] What are the characteristics of God as shown through this part of Gideon's life?

Is God steadfast, faithful, just, trustworthy, nurturing, kind, gentle, or strong? What do you see revealed about His nature in this passage of Scripture?

_____

_____

_____

_____

_____

[ ] What are the promises of God as shown through this chapter?

Write any observations, key words, or questions you have as you ponder the passage If you have time, you may want to do another word study.

_____

_____

_____

_____

_____

_____

_____

_____

DIGGING DEEPER: EPHESIANS 6

[ ] Read Ephesians 6

[ ] Imagine

Insert yourself in the scene. Imagine you are there. What is happening? What do you notice?

_____

_____

_____

_____

_____

_____

_____

_____

_____

_____

_____

[ ] Write down any general thoughts or questions you have as
you read the verses today.

_____

_____

_____

_____

_____

_____

_____

_____

A Story
of Courage

DAY FOUR

Reading Passage
Judges chapter 7

 TODAY'S DECLARE PRACTICE *Listen* 🎧

Remember to take a moment to ENGAGE as you prepare to listen: toss, catch, invite, open, expect. Invite the Words of Scripture and the Words of God to speak personally into your mind and heart. Remember that God's voice will never accuse you. He may bring gentle conviction, and that can cause some grief, but God always brings hope.

Listening can be pursued for several days, and in fact, God will probably speak unexpectedly at random times of day or night as His revelation is released to you. Ask these questions as you listen to God's voice:

[ ] How does this part of Gideon's story apply to me?

_____

_____

_____

_____

_____

_____

_____

_____

HAVE A LITTLE MORE TIME?

[ ] Ponder and pray: Dear Lord, what does it mean to be
strong in you? Please show me the ways I seek strength
in places or people other than you. Do these substitute
saviors really give me power? How can I become more
confident in your power?

_____

_____

_____

_____

_____

_____

DIGGING DEEPER: EPHESIANS 6

[ ] Read Ephesians 6

[ ] Listen

Ask yourself: how do these verses apply to me? What is the connection between obedience and strength?

_____

_____

_____

_____

_____

_____

[ ] Write down any general thoughts or questions you have as you read the verses today.

_____

_____

_____

_____

_____

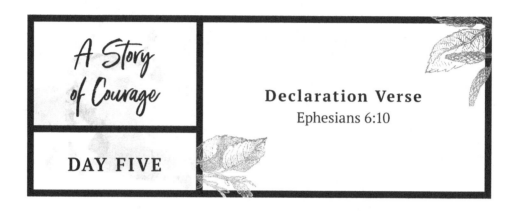

A Story of Courage

DAY FIVE

Declaration Verse
Ephesians 6:10

 TODAY'S DECLARE PRACTICE *Declare*

Write out a declaration of what you have received as you
meditated on the Word. This can be a statement of God's
promise to you, an affirmation of the healing that He has
given you, or a proclamation of a truth that has become
real to you. A declaration can include Scripture, your own
words, or some of each.

_____

_____

_____

_____

_____

_____

REFLECT ON YOUR WEEK 📅

Write out Ephesians 6:10 by hand if you memorized it or
summarize the Declaration Verse in your own words below.

_____

_____

_____

_____

_____

Spend a few minutes documenting your insights, "a-ha"
moments, and revelations from this week of digging into
the Bible.

_____

_____

_____

_____

_____

_____

_____

Week Three: Discussion Topics

We provide discussion topics to help facilitate conversations with friends as you enjoy this study together, or you can ponder these questions as a personal reflection. Even if you are not able to meet up with others, you're invited to join us in our private Facebook Group at facebook.com/groups/flourishgathering/

1. Do you have any thoughts or reactions to this week's devotional? Here are two passages to inspire conversation:

    "Self-sufficiency is a handicap which causes us to rely in our own strength. When God strips us of our self-reliance, it forces us to place our full confidence in God and not in ourselves. Have you experienced this in your life?" (page 85)

    "I always wondered what it meant to be 'strong in the Lord.' I discovered that strength has nothing to do with physical abilities or the size of your army. Godly strength comes from confidence in who God is and surrender to His power, not ours." (page 85)

2. Was there a special insight you gained from the **Investigate** practice? Perhaps an interesting word study, cross reference, or commentary?

3. What happened when you used your **Imagination**? What did you discover about the context of this chapter or book of the Bible? If you had time, did you gain insight into the character or promises of God?

4. Did God speak something special that you would like to share as you **Listened**?

5. What is your **Declaration**? How can we pray for you in this regard?

6. How can we support one another this week? Prayer requests? Praise reports?

Notes

Notes

WEEK FOUR

A Story of Perseverance

DECLARATION VERSE

*"But we have this precious treasure, the good news
about salvation, in unworthy earthen vessels of
human frailty, so that the grandeur and surpassing
greatness of the power will be shown to be from
God—His sufficiency—and not from ourselves."*
2 Corinthians 4:7 (AMP)

The Power Comes from God

"*There's no hope, his condition simply will not improve.*"

The doctor's words sucked the air out of the room as quickly as they tumbled off his lips. I began to feel lightheaded and excused myself while my husband and the doctor spoke about my husband's chronic condition.

As I stepped outside into the steamy summer afternoon, I began to cry uncontrollably. The burdens of this dreadful season had chipped away at my sense of purpose and hope. As the tears fell and my frustrations welled up inside me, I heard the Lord whisper to my heart.

"Jenny, I've called you to be confident and courageous in this battle."

Immediately my excuses began. I didn't "*feel*" confident and courageous. I felt defeated and deflated. I had been struggling with allowing my *feelings* to be moved and manipulated by sight. Everything I saw around me scared me. The news scared me. The stories I heard of struggles from friends and family scared me. The things that were happening in my life scared me. *The unknown really scared me!*

Right then, I posed a question to the Lord: *God, show me how to remain confident in you during this battle. Show me how to persevere.*

Have you walked through a season where everything you saw before you looked hopeless? You question if your prayers are being heard. You ask yourself if God is at work. You wonder if you're walking this journey alone.

Over the next several weeks, the Lord began to show me what a confident and courageous heart looks like. In order to fully grasp what it means to be courageous and confident in the Lord (Ephesians 6:10), we must first examine what the opposite of courage and confidence looks like.

We're going to visit another hero of the faith: King David. David's story throughout the Scriptures is one of courage, perseverance, and faith. He embodies a confident and courageous heart. However, we're going to see David during a time when he allowed his earthly sight to rule over his heart.

In 1 Chronicles 21, David asks his men to take a census of the army. As the commander in chief, it seems reasonable to find out how many men he has available to fight for the country. On the surface this doesn't seem like an unreasonable request, yet we find David's motives deceive him.

By counting the Israelite men, David places his faith in the strength of his army. He is beginning to trust more in military power than in the power of God. Yikes! *Oh, how my heart can relate to David.*

Recently I found a journal entry from several years ago. It was during the same time my husband was in the thick of his storm. There was no light at the end of the tunnel and no end in sight to his suffering.

I penned these words one night:

One week from today we will go to yet another neurologist appointment. I'm not sure how many more I can take. It's been two-and-a-half years. Two years of figuring this out, praying, fasting, doctors, medicines. Two years of patience, tear-soaked prayers, running to the altar, asking why, anger, denial, impatience, and being broken. Yet, recently something happened inside my heart....it all ended, the striving, the trying to figure it out, the pleading with God. I've chosen to surrender.

For over two years I placed my trust in the strength of my "army" of doctors and new medicines; however, like David my heart wasn't in the right place. My confidence was in my strength and abilities and those around me instead of the power of God.

In Paul's letter to the Corinthians, we find a promise, a guiding light:

"But we have this precious treasure, the good news about salvation, in unworthy earthen vessels of

human frailty, so that the grandeur and surpassing
greatness of the power will be shown to be from
God—His sufficiency—and not from ourselves."
2 Corinthians 4:7 (AMP)

Confidence and courage lie in acknowledging our human frailty--rejoicing in it even as Paul describes—and allowing God's mighty power not our own to fight our battles. Courage comes when we raise the white flag and surrender our "armies" of self-sufficiency. Confidence arrives when we fix our eyes on the power of God in our lives and not in what we see.

God-dependency is all about our perspective. It's about what we choose to "see." Will we look at our earthly treasures like possessions and positions as having the power to save or will we allow the power of God to be revealed in our lives?

Through the story of Gideon, we see a man who understands his place in God's greater story. He understands courage and confidence come when you lay down your strength in exchange for God's strength. He knows doubts, insecurities and fear, yet he answers the call to be courageous and strong in the Lord, not in himself.

What does this say to us? Instead of being women who shout, "She believed she could, so she did," our declaration is *"She believed she could, and so He did!"* All our battles are opportunities for God to demonstrate His power and presence in and through us.

The experience of my husband's chronic illness taught me that when I allow God to work and stop striving in my own sufficiency, I can see God's peace and presence during the battle. God is good and He longs for us to see His glory and His outstretched hand in the chaos of our lives, in our families, and in our world.

Our stories aren't easy, the roads we travel are often broken. Our hearts long to see the promises of God fulfilled. Yet, sometimes during the suffering, the waiting, the unknown, we must choose to see . . . and we must choose to believe in the grandeur and surpassing greatness of the power of God!

Jenny

ENGAGE Prayer Method

The DECLARE Bible Study Approach begins by engaging or tuning your ears and heart to God's voice. The ENGAGE Prayer Method prepares your heart and mind to hear:

TOSS: Throw your cares on God. Let Him bear your burdens. *Psalm 55:22*

CATCH: Receive the peace that surpasses all understanding. *Philippians 4:7*

INVITE: Take every thought captive. Invite clarity and focus. Refuse confusion, distraction, or double-mindedness. *2 Corinthians 10:5*

OPEN: Ask God if you have turned away or closed your heart to anyone. Release the offense, open your heart, and give the situation into God's care. *Psalm 139:23*

EXPECT: Tell God that you are looking forward to hearing from Him. Let the excitement of time in His presence build expectation in your heart. *Habakkuk 2:1*

A Story of Perseverance

DAY ONE

Declaration Verse

"But we have this precious treasure, the good news about salvation, in unworthy earthen vessels of human frailty, so that the grandeur and surpassing greatness of the power will be shown to be from God—His sufficiency— and not from ourselves."

2 Corinthians 4:7 (AMP)

 TODAY'S DECLARE PRACTICE *Read & Write*

[ ] Read 2 Corinthians 4:7 slowly once or twice, even out loud if you are able.

[ ] Write 2 Corinthians 4:6-7 in the space below. *Feel free to get creative!*

_____

_____

_____

_____

_____

_____

HAVE A LITTLE MORE TIME?

[ ] Read 2 Corinthians chapter 4 for context. Write out a few
observations:

_____

_____

_____

_____

_____

_____

_____

[ ] Read 2 Corinthians 4:7 in another Bible translation. Do you
notice any differences? Write your observations.

_____

_____

_____

_____

_____

_____

DIGGING DEEPER: JUDGES 8

[ ] Read Judges chapter 8

[ ] Read and Write

Write any verse that stands out to you as you read the passage.

_____

_____

_____

_____

_____

[ ] Write down any general thoughts or questions you have as you read the verses today.

_____

_____

_____

_____

_____

A Story
of Perseverance

DAY TWO

Declaration Verse
2 Corinthians 4:7

 TODAY'S DECLARE PRACTICE *Investigate*

Today we begin looking deeper into the Declaration Verse. Investigate as little or as much as time allows. Online resources like BibleGateway.com or BlueLetterBible.org will help you during your investigation.

[ ] Conduct a Word Study: Part One

Read the Declaration Verse. Spend a few minutes highlighting any words you want to research more. Write these words below.

_____

_____

_____

_____

_____

_____

_____

[ ] Conduct a Word Study: Part Two

Using BlueLetterBible.org or another online resource, choose a word you selected above to conduct your word study. This is as simple as looking up the original Greek or Hebrew word, reading the definitions of that word, and looking at how it is used in other verses in the Bible.

Record the results of your word study here.

_____

_____

_____

_____

_____

_____

 HAVE A LITTLE MORE TIME?

[ ] Read any of the following cross references for 2 Corinthians 4:7:

† John 16:33

† 1 Corinthians 2:4-5

† Deuteronomy 8:16-18

Reading cross references will help you better understand a verse, word, or principle. What did you discover? Write your insights.

_____

_____

_____

_____

_____

_____

_____

[ ] Read a commentary. A commentary is a collection of explanatory notes that a Bible scholar has written about scripture. You can find these online. A good place to begin is Matthew Henry, C.H. Spurgeon, or David Guzik.

Write any observations, quotes, or notes.

_____

_____

_____

_____

_____

_____

_____

_____

_____

_____

_____

_____

_____

DIGGING DEEPER: JUDGES 8

[ ] Read Judges chapter 8

[ ] Investigate

Highlight a couple of key words that stand out to you in the verses you read. Using BlueLetterBible.org look up the Greek or Hebrew word and definition of one of those words.

Write your findings below.

_____

_____

_____

_____

_____

_____

_____

_____

_____

_____

_____

_____

[ ] Write down any general thoughts or questions you have as
    you read the verses today.

_____

_____

_____

_____

_____

_____

_____

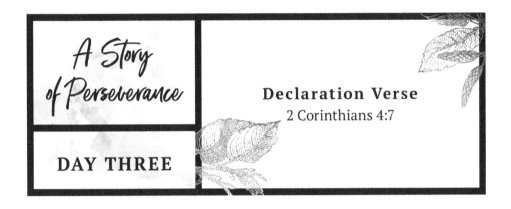

A Story of Perseverance

DAY THREE

Declaration Verse
2 Corinthians 4:7

 TODAY'S DECLARE PRACTICE *Imagine*

Remember to ENGAGE as you prepare to imagine: toss, catch, invite, open, expect. Invite the Words of Scripture and the Words of God to speak personally into your mind and heart.

[ ] Read 2 Corinthians chapter 4

Use your imagination and all your senses to be present in the scene.

[ ] How does God's power show through in my human frailty?

_____

_____

_____

_____

_____

_____

_____

[ ] What in me needs to surrender to you so I can receive Jesus'
resurrection life?

_____

_____

_____

_____

_____

_____

[ ] How do I focus my eyes on the seen rather than the unseen?
What would life be like if I kept my eyes on what is eternal
rather than what is temporary?

_____

_____

_____

_____

_____

_____

_____

_____

_____

_____

_____

HAVE A LITTLE MORE TIME?

[ ] What are the characteristics of God as shown through the Declaration Verse?

Is He steadfast, faithful, just, trustworthy, nurturing, kind, gentle, or strong? What do you see revealed about His nature in this passage of Scripture?

_____

_____

_____

_____

_____

_____

_____

_____

_____

_____

_____

_____

_____

_____

[ ] What are the promises of God as shown through the
Declaration Verse?

Write any observations, key words, or questions you have
as you ponder the Declaration Verse. If you have time, you
may want to do another word study.

_____

_____

_____

_____

_____

_____

_____

_____

DIGGING DEEPER: JUDGES 8

[ ] Read Judges chapter 8

[ ] Imagine

Insert yourself in the scene. Imagine you are there. What is happening? What do you notice?

_____

_____

_____

_____

_____

[ ] Write down any general thoughts or questions you have as you read the verses today.

_____

_____

_____

_____

_____

Declaration Verse
2 Corinthians 4:7

DAY FOUR

 TODAY'S DECLARE PRACTICE Listen

Remember to take a moment to ENGAGE as you prepare to listen: toss, catch, invite, open, expect. Invite the Words of Scripture and the Words of God to speak personally into your mind and heart. Remember that God's voice will never accuse you. He may bring gentle conviction, and that can cause some grief, but God always brings hope.

Listening can be pursued for several days, and in fact, God will probably speak unexpectedly at random times of day or night as His revelation is released to you. Ask these questions as you listen to God's voice:

[ ] How do I find my strength in you and not in myself or others?

_____

_____

🌱 HAVE A LITTLE MORE TIME?

[ ] Ponder and pray: What needs to yield in my heart and
   mind so that I can let your power be revealed in my life?

DIGGING DEEPER: JUDGES 8

[ ] Read Judges chapter 8

[ ] Listen

Ask yourself: how does this part of Gideon's story apply to me?
What does God want to speak to me through these verses?

_____

_____

_____

_____

_____

_____

[ ] Write down any general thoughts or questions you have as
you read the verses.

_____

_____

_____

_____

_____

_____

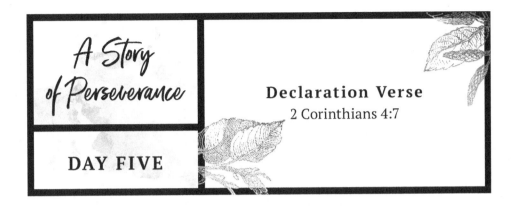

A Story of Perseverance

DAY FIVE

Declaration Verse
2 Corinthians 4:7

 TODAY'S DECLARE PRACTICE *Declare*

Write out a declaration of what you have received as you meditated on the Word. This can be a statement of God's promise to you, an affirmation of the healing that He has given you, or a proclamation of a truth that has become real to you. A declaration can include Scripture, your own words, or some of each.

_____

_____

_____

_____

_____

_____

_____

_____

_____

_____

_____

_____

REFLECT ON YOUR WEEK 📅

Write out 2 Corinthians 4:7 by hand if you memorized it
or summarize the Declaration Verse in your own words
below.

_____

_____

_____

_____

_____

_____

_____

Spend a few minutes documenting your insights, "a-ha" moments, and revelations from this week of digging into the Bible.

_____

_____

_____

_____

_____

_____

_____

_____

_____

_____

_____

_____

_____

_____

Week Four: Discussion Topics

We provide discussion topics to help facilitate conversations with friends as you enjoy this study together, or you can ponder these questions as a personal reflection. Even if you are not able to meet up with others, you're invited to join us in our private Facebook Group at facebook.com/groups/flourishgathering/

1. Do you have any thoughts or reactions to this week's devotional? Here are two passages to inspire conversation:

    "Immediately my excuses began. I didn't feel confident and courageous. I felt defeated and deflated. Everything I saw around me scared me. The news scared me. The things that were happening in my life scared me. The unknown really scared me! Have you been there?" (page 113)

    "Confidence and courage lie in acknowledging our human frailty--rejoicing in it even as Paul describes--and allowing God's mighty power to fight our battles. Courage comes when we raise the white flag and surrender our 'armies' of self-sufficiency." (page 116)

2. Was there a special insight you gained from the
    Investigate practice? Perhaps an interesting
    word study, cross reference, or commentary?

3. What happened when you used your **Imagination**?
    What did you discover about the context of
    this chapter or book of the Bible? If you had
    time, did you gain insight into the character or
    promises of God?

4. Did God speak something special that you would
    like to share as you **Listened**?

5. What is your **Declaration**? How can we pray for
    you in this regard?

6. How can we support one another this week?
    Prayer requests? Praise reports?

Notes

Notes

_____

_____

_____

_____

_____

_____

_____

_____

_____

_____

_____

_____

_____

_____

_____

_____

I Can Because He Can

We stand on tiptoe, eager to see how God reveals the power of your story as His Story. When we recognize the grandeur and surpassing greatness of His power in each season of our lives, it stirs a desire to share our stories with others. Your life's trials and joys are not designed to be hidden away, but to shine as evidence of God's goodness. The testimony of a sister is a fountain of cool water refreshing a weary soul.

> *"It is written: 'I believed; therefore I have spoken.'*
> *Since we have that same spirit of faith, we also*
> *believe and therefore speak."* 2 Corinthians 4:13

When you believe, it compels you to speak. Each season of your life testifies to His sufficiency, greatness and power. So why do the forces of evil make us ashamed to share our true selves with transparency? Why is vulnerability so frightening?

Your testimony washed by the blood of Jesus holds the power to conquer the enemy. (Revelation 12:11) Your stories threaten to tear down the strongholds of evil. Satan is terrified of the powerful potential contained in our God Stories. He does everything he can to silence us. We are silenced by fears that heavy stories are too shameful and light stories are too simple. But is there any story redeemed by the blood that cannot shine for God's glory?

Consider Gideon's life. We honor him for saving Israel from the heavy hand of the Midianites, but he is still an imperfect human being trying his best to follow his Lord. Despite his courageous victories, Gideon makes a misstep. When the fighting ends, the people ask him to become king of Israel. Will he be lured to take this position of power? No, he stands strong, reminding the people that God alone is their king.

But then Gideon has an unguarded thought: I will make a gold ephod to celebrate our victory. This doesn't sound so bad, except the fruit of this action has deadly consequences. The golden ephod becomes an idol: "All Israel prostituted themselves by worshiping [the ephod] there, and it became a snare to Gideon and his family." (Judges 8:27)

After his faithful obedience and personal sacrifice, Gideon makes a choice with negative consequences for his people, and yet this mistake does not disqualify him from showing up by name in the Hebrews 11 "hall of fame." God does not expect perfection, just humility.

All through Scripture, we find stories of people trying to walk in God's way. Although our human struggle doesn't cause God to give up on us, it can cause us to give up on ourselves. Life is messy! How do we understand the imperfection of our human experience?

The starting place is God's never failing, never ending, and forever steadfast love. By grace, He writes a story of redemption that shines within the parts of our story we're proud of, but His purpose also radiates within the parts we're ashamed of. In fact, His glorious light shines more brightly in the darkness, doesn't it?

Nothing in your story is too shameful for the light. We don't suggest that every detail needs to be written down or shared with others, but the first step is to talk with God about it and allow Him to reveal His salvation and restoration in every season of your life.

Let Him show you how He rescued you. When you process your stories with Jesus, and invite Him to remove the shame and guilt, He will unveil every detail of your life as a testimony of His faithfulness. He is everywhere, in everything, sovereign and good:

> *If I go up to the heavens, you are there;*
> *if I make my bed in the depths, you are there.*
> *If I rise on the wings of the dawn,*
> *if I settle on the far side of the sea,*
> *even there your hand will guide me,*
> *your right hand will hold me fast.*
>
> Psalm 139: 8-10

When you see the eternal glory God reveals in your testimony, it stirs a desire to shout it out. *My story is His Story!* Nothing is by accident. Every single event, decision, and action reveals your life as a modern-day gospel for this generation. Your life has been purchased by His blood, and you offer yourself a living sacrifice, poured out as an offering with Christ.

> *"So we fix our eyes not on what is seen, but on what is unseen, since what is seen is temporary, but what is unseen is eternal."* 2 Corinthians 4:18

We pray that you see your story in light of eternity. It is not yours alone, but His, for it was purchased at a great price.

I can because God can.

With *"I can"* on your lips, your story of purpose, your story of overcoming is revealed daily in the pages of your life. May you find faith, courage and perseverance to live your story as His Story.

Jenny & Mindy

A little bit about Flourish

Flourish is a gathering of women who passionately pursue God and His Word. We encourage one another through genuine, transparent relationships which equip us to thrive where we are planted and impact our world for the glory of God.

We believe that the power of God's Word revealed by the Spirit changes lives. In relationship with God and with one another, we are strengthened to overcome hindrances in our journey. Flourish is dedicated to bringing God's Word to life in the 21st Century by encouraging women that the Word is alive, active, and powerful today.

Now here's our purpose spelled out in regular talk.

We want more of God, so we dig into His Word. We can't survive without Him. We can't survive without you either.

You can leave your mask at the door because real life is messy, and no one here is pretending to have it all together

At Flourish we...

ENCOURAGE

We share real stories of real life with transparency and honesty, always pointing to the promises found in God's Word.

EQUIP

Flourish provides tools and resources that are grounded in the Word of God. Our community provides a safe place to learn and to grow.

ACTIVATE

We seek God in community because, when the rubber hits the road, we want to see evidence of God's life in our relationships.

About the Authors

Meet Mindy . .

Mindy Kiker is a committed Floridian, enjoying a quiet woodland home that she and her husband built to shelter their four boisterous boys. Born in Tucson, Arizona, Mindy's magical childhood included a four-year hiatus on the big island of Hawaii where she danced the hula, and later helped with the family marina in Cedar Key where she learned to cast net and sail the Gulf of Mexico. The Kikers spent the 1990s in South Africa, returning with their brood for a sabbatical year in 2012 to reconnect with beloved friends and favorite places.

Now that Mindy's spring-chicken days are drawing to a close, she has accepted her role as an "older" woman (it's all relative) cheering others on in life's journey. A favorite verse that motivates her to keep pressing into God and encouraging her friends to do the same is *Galatians 5:1, "It is for freedom that Christ has set us free. Stand firm, then, and do not let yourselves be burdened again by a yoke of slavery."*

And Jenny. . .

Jenny Kochert was born and raised in sunny South Florida. Although she took full advantage of big-city life growing up, she longed to move to a quieter town, and college provided the perfect excuse! After graduating from the University of Florida, Jenny followed in the family footsteps and became a private investigator (yes, you read that right!), opening her own agency in 2005.

However, once she became a mom to her daughter, Sophia, she turned in her badge, and settled at home, now home schooling her daughter. Jenny, her husband Ryan, and daughter Sophia now live in Northern Kentucky where they serve in ministry together as a family. God has put a story on her lips and a passion in her heart to encourage women, and she is thrilled that she gets to do that each and every day.

Thank you

For Flourishing with Us!

Connect with us on Facebook
@Flourishgathering
@Flourishwriters

†

Contact us
info@flourishgathering.com

†

Visit us
Flourishgathering.com
Flourishwriters.com

Made in the USA
Columbia, SC
24 June 2019